Cheating
at
CONKERS

Poems chosen by
David Orme

Illustrated by *Derek Collin*

 LONGMAN

Contents

* This poem was written when the poet was still at school

 How to Use This Book

Thirteen Things to Do With a Poem

Roll it into a telescope and peep through it
Read it to the cat
Cut two holes in it, put your fingers through
    and make the poem dance
Tie it to a balloon and launch it
Send it to your best friend
Send it to your worst enemy
Wrap a sweet in it and throw it to your gran
Cut it up and use the words to make a kite tail
Lay the words end to end and see how many beans
    it takes to cover them
Bake it in a fortune cookie
Keep it inside your sock for a day
Fold it into a paper boat and send it exploring
    down a river
Make up silly questions about it to ask your teacher!

124

Rita Ray

A t S c h o o l

Wet Playtime

hungry chatter
friendly chatter
pitter patter
what's the matter?
tattered textbooks
skim like skates
bad boys batter
last week's mates
watch the rain
just drench the playground
blowing paper
round and round.
Here inside
the jigsaws clatter
eat those crisps
they'll make you fatter
drop your juice
and dodge the splatter
teacher's coming
quick let's scatter
pitter patter
nitter natter
friendly chatter
what's the matter?

Dave Ward

The Champion

Step forward, Billy Green,
Pride of the school!
Billy's done it once again,
Billy's really cool.
Mornings in Assembly,
He sings the wrong tune;
But every year he's champion
At the Egg and Spoon.

Who's that training
Behind the canteen,
Pebbles balanced on a stick?
That's Billy Green:
Dodging and weaving.
Darting round about
– Serious training.
Better watch out.

Doesn't like playing Chess,
Says it hurts his brain;
Doesn't like Soccer,
Especially in the rain;
Doesn't like Cross-Country,
Says it hurts his feet;
But once a year on Sports Day,
He's the one to beat.

Look at that footwork!
Look at those legs!
Look at that dexterity,
He never breaks the eggs!
Such an egg and spoon race
Was surely never seen:
Come up here and take your
   prize,
Champion Billy Green.

Tony Charles

133

Bee Quiet

A bee buzzed into the classroom,
a titchy buzzing machine,
a lumbering, bumbling bumble-bee,
a flying butter bean,

with a black and yellow jersey on,
madly flapping the air
with a pair of much-too-diddy wings.
"Nobody move!" said Sir.

We were stiller than ever we'd been before,
Stiller than statues we were.
"If no silly person annoys it
it'll fly away." said Sir.

It blundered into the gerbils' cage,
then over the tank it hovered
where Fred, our placid goldfish, swims
who didn't seem much bothered.

At last it found the window
and into the sunlight it flew,
chuffed to be out in the open
where the honeysuckle grew. 112

"Now I know what I should do
when you lot make a din:
bring me in a bumble-bee!"
said Sir with a sarky grin.

This afternoon was something else;
in the middle of doing Spelling
a wasp flew into the classroom:
soon everyone was yelling,

was dodging about and ducking it.
Before the beast had gone
there was panic, there was mutiny,
it dive-bombed every one.

And there was Sir shouting
"Nobody move! Stay cool!"
Then the wasp flew at him like a dart
and buzzed him out of school.

Matt Simpson

A Teacher Asked a Kid One Day

"Why are you so thick,
My lad,
Why can't you be like Dick?
Brains bursting from his ears,
Understanding everything,
Remembering all he hears.
Instead you sit,
At the back of the class,
All on your own,
Waiting for the bell to go,
So you can go off home."

David Genn

How Come

How come in the big school I'm little,
When in the little school I was big?
There I was responsible,
Here I'm just a kid.
Being first should mean you're better,
Now I'm the last in every queue.
Growing up is very difficult.
I think so, don't you?

SuAndi

The Dinner Lady

I'm the dinner lady
serving up stew.
I'm the dinner lady
"how do you do?"
I'm the dinner lady:
"NOT SO MUCH NOISE!
Let's have a bit of quiet,
girls and boys.
Get back Peter
and wait your turn."
I don't earn much
but it's all I earn.
"Amanda, you mustn't
pick on Jane.
I've told you before –
I won't tell you again."
At home I've got
four kids of my own.
"Michael, why are you sitting all
alone?
You don't look well –
are you feeling upset?
Come over here
and tell me, my pet.
Cheer up now,
let me dry your tears."

I'm the dinner lady
and I've been here twenty years.
I get out the plates,
I stack and wash and dry,
I serve up ice cream
and apple pie.
Then, when the kids are gone
and I've swept the floor,
I put on my coat
and I walk out the door
and I go back home
and I pour a cup of tea
and I'm not the dinner lady:
Oh no! I'm ME.

Charles Thomson

10

On the Way Home

Bag Flinging

Two friends,
stand exactly shouting distance apart.
On the word, "Go!"
School bags are simultaneously flung
across the shouting distance

And caught.

World record at time of writing.
Forty nine consecutive flings.
But

On the fiftieth fling
The two school bags
met – mid air
fell fast

Bag A
suffered only minor cuts and bruises
But Bag B
lay lifeless
a concussed carrier
with a split zip
through which a broken ruler poked.

And there were serious internal injuries;
A lacerated lunch box
– with complications –
Perforation of the yoghurt pot;
with consequent leakage over
the adjacent football shorts.

Bag B's final fling.

John Coldwell

How to Cheat at Conkers and Win

Find a stone, a good heavy one
paint it conker colour
smash your opponent's conker
  to bits.

Find a snooker ball
drill a hole and fit the string
watch it win.

Try the same idea
with a mechanical digger.

Dynamite is good.
It will blow the opposing conker
to pieces.

Disguise your local conker trees
by painting them as palms.

Your opponent will think
all the conkers are coconuts
and run out of supplies very
  soon.

Just as your conker
is about to be hit, shout
"Fire!" "Police" "Isn't that
  Elvis?"
Confused and surprised they will
  miss.

Dig a hole in the yard
and cover it with a sack.
Encourage the other player to
  step on it.
As they disappear shout "I've
  won".

Just as your opponent
is about to mash your best 99er
put on a deep sea diving suit.
Then jump up and down very
  hard
which will tilt the balance of the
  planet
thus causing huge tidal waves
to crash over the landscape
and wash your opponent away.

That should do it.
David Harmer

Greengrocer

I went into the greengrocer's:
the vegetables and the fruit
were all piled neatly in their boxes
and a large watermelon lay in the corner.

I couldn't see the greengrocer.
The shop smelt ripe and drowsy. I put
three bananas in a paper bag. It was
so still and silent I felt watched.
The mushrooms looked like knee bones.
The watermelon lay contented in the corner.

What had happened to the greengrocer?
I took some carrots. I stuffed
plastic bags with spinach,
with the long green teeth of okra,
with courgettes like tiny truncheons.
The watermelon lay big-bellied in the corner.

There was no sign of the greengrocer.
I called out, I waited, then I left
money by the till and went towards the door.
The enormous watermelon in the corner
snored.

Dave Calder

Briefing

They will be looking
for a shifty,
suspicious character
who will
swap identical cases
in the crowded lounge
and then melt
into the background.

Therefore you must wear
a large baggy
green and lilac striped suit,
red nose
and bright yellow bowler.
Your carrier bag
will be marked
VERY TOP SECRET.

As you lift the black
shiny briefcase
leave the brown carrier
with the red,
white and blue balloons
fully inflated.
Dance your way
to the exit while
singing at
the top of your voice.
No need to worry
about security.
Take this pistol.
Before you set off,
fill it with water.

John C Desmond

Big Beefy Biff the Beef Burger Burglar

Meet big beefy Biff the beef burger burglar
burgling big beefy burgers of beef.
Boldly he burgles the biggest beef burgers
big beefy Biff the biggest meat thief.

He battered and broke in the Big Beefy Burger Bar
burgling burgers in bright broad daylight
biting the best biggest brown buttered breadbuns
bagging the beefiest burgers in sight.

He bit bits of burgers and bit bits of breadbuns
busily biting between and beneath.
From breakfast he battled and binged beef and breadcrumbs
belching big burps that baffled belief.

Big beefy Biff the beef burger burglar
burgling big beefy burgers of beef.
Big beefy Biff the beef burger burglar
Big beefy Biff the beef burger thief.

Paul Cookson

Downpour

The street fizzes.
You're caught without a coat.
Dive in that teeming doorway
Make friends or get soaked.

Litter pasted to the pavement
Like posters to a wall.
A coke-can shooting rapids in the gutter
To a drain's whirlpool.

A dog's ears flapped down like shutters
On the sides of its face.
A cat staring from a window
As if it's raining giant mice.

Lorries plough furrows through puddles
Like tractors over fields.
Cars lash by
Making water weals.

Cyclists wear yellow tents –
Poke their heads up from inside.
They may look half-soaked
But they're keeping all dry.

There are drum-roll rumbles
On the roofs of parked vans.
Babies do a wide-eyed jive
To the rhythm on their prams.

People sprinting to bus shelters
Wearing newspaper hats
Hair-dos undone
Hang like the tails of rats.

Water ripples like curtains
Falling from house roofs
Come down on an audience
Dumfounded and enthused.

Because
It's
A
Downpour
Casting wet spells
A deluge
And a drencher
A cloudburst as well
A thunderstorm
Driving torrential rain
Precipitation
Is too dry a name
It's a monsoon

A soaker
And a pelter too
That sheets and drops buckets
Down to wet you.

We get beaten by the weather,
It wins every time.
Well, when we looked out this
   morning
The outlook was fine.

                    Stephen Clarke

Points of View

"What shape is water?" the duckling asked
As he swam with his Mum by his side.
"It's round and it's flat, any duck can see that,
And it's long and it's deep and it's wide.

"What shape is water?" the young minnow said
As he swam in the pond with his pop.
"Now I don't know that, but it's not round or flat,
And watch out for the ducks at the top."

Ian Larmont

Garden Enthusiasts

Prowling like a sly pair of careful thieves
the tabbies quietly stalk the pile of leaves,

quite slow at first, caught up in frenzy next, then quick
to pounce and rustle, sift the spoils – acorn or stick,

a fallen hazelnut the squirrels overlooked – each cat
tunnels a way into the moist autumnal brownness that

flies from sleek fur in plentiful and mottled flurry: one might think
treasure lay buried there, most pleasurable mulch in which to sink.

Alexis Lykiard

Indoors

The House That ...

Ours is not the house that Jack built.
The roof leaks,
The lights won't work,
And under the squeaking floorboards
    spiders lurk.

Ours is not the house that Jack built.
The doors creak,
The TV's bust
And even the dog's got a bad case
    of rust.

Ours is not the house that Jack built.
The chimney's blocked,
The loo won't flush,
The Hoover's naffed so we
    use a brush.

Ours is not the house that Jack built.
The walls wobble,
The car won't start
And the fitted wardrobe's
    falling apart.

But Dad's going to fix it all real soon
(Mum's so excited she's over the moon).
He'll roll up his sleeves, be on the attack —
When Jack next door brings his tool box back.

Mel Lewis

My Party

Come to my party on Christmas Eve
in my rented air balloon.
Well, it's really a Zeppelin,
and at midnight you've got to leave.

Why? Because it's Christmas.
How do you get up there?
Hitch a ride on a helicopter.
Do it, and don't make a fuss,

and don't be late, or the angels
won't appear in their feathers
or their space suit evening wear,
and the food will go to the gulls.
The food? There'll be larks' eggs
and flying fish, and roast crow.
(Horrible? How do you know?)
And specially imported moon figs.

Oh, and coke made with rain.
What about music? The stars
helped along by meteors
will cobble together a tune.

No more questions? Good.
Write it in the diary, then,
and spread the news to a friend
immediately. Is that understood?

Matthew Sweeney

Christmas Stocking

Wake up, sleepysock!
Six o'clock
And time to yawn.

What's this on top?
A bumpelwopper –
(Great! I'll eat that first,)
A plunkey
And some crillies
(Though I've still got last year's somewhere,)
Yes! a tootleburst,
A pack of prinkles
And a moomeroomer.
So
To the toe
And the usual fatsuma.

Thank you, emptysock.
It's now six-ten.
Time to go back to sleep again.

Sue Cowling

Me and My Granny

My granny
always tells the truth
so whenever I call round
to help her do her shopping
she'll say, *Sit down. I'll not be a minute.*
And you know, she never is.
She can be 3 minutes, 7, 11 and half minutes,
even half an hour once
but she's never ever been a minute.

My granny
can see into the future
so whenever she drops a dish or a cup
then sits on her glasses and snaps the frame in two
she'll say, *There'll be a third –*
something else'll get broken.
And do you know, it always does.
Sometimes we have to wait a month or even more,
but it always does.

My granny
knows where everything is
so whenever I lose anything
and I tell her I've hunted high and low
she'll say, *Keep looking, love, because you know it'll be*
in the last place you look.

So I go on looking, looking, looking
till I think I've turned the whole house upside down
and there it is – always in the very last place.

David Horner

A Grandmother's Rhyme

Look at me! What do you see?
An old crone like a gnarled tree
bent over double as if in the grip
of a terrible storm? It makes me flip
to see pictures of granny dowdily dressed
(probably corsets and bloomers and vest
in layers under her long skirt, and all
topped by a knitted woollen shawl).
And Granddad's image isn't fair –
whiskery, toothless, not much hair.

We don't suddenly shuffle and doze
with specs slipping down a wrinkled nose;
we don't dress in Victorian gear
and hold a trumpet to one ear;

we don't nod in a chair and snore
and never go anywhere, and what's more
we don't turn vague and mild and good
just because of grandparenthood –

and if that state were such a curse
I'd have no wit left for writing verse.

Pamela Gillilan

Dad's Hiding in the Shed

Dad's hiding in the shed.
He's made me swear
Not to tell Mum
That he's hiding in there.

She was having a lie-down
With the curtains drawn.
We were playing cricket
Out on the lawn.

The scores were level.
It was really tense.
Dad had just hit a six
Right over the fence.

I bowled the next ball
As fast as I could.
Dad tried it again
As I knew he would.

He missed and the ball
Struck him hard on the toe.
He cried out in pain
And, as he did so,

He let go of the bat.
It flew up in an arc
And crashed through the window
Where Mum lay in the dark.

Dad's hiding in the shed.
He's made me swear
Not to tell Mum
That he's hiding in there.

John Foster

On the Tenth of February

My brother brought the snowman in
to keep him warm.

He sat him in the chair
by the fire.

The chair that dad likes.

The snowman sat there,
sweating.
His nose began to slip away.

My dad came in from work,
freezing.

The snowman was wearing
Uncle Frank's old hat.

My dad doesn't like Uncle Frank.

My dad's glasses steamed up
in the warm room.

"Hello, Frank,"
he said to the snowman,

"When are you going to give me
that ten quid you owe me?"

The snowman collapsed
in a puddle all over the carpet.

My dad stared
at the empty chair
and said,

"It's okay Frank,
pay me whenever you like.
It's only money."

Ian McMillan

My Dog's First Poem

(To be read aloud in a dog's voice.)

My barking drives them
    up the wall.
I chew the carpet
    in the hall.
I love to chase
    a bouncing b...   ... banana?

Everywhere I leave
    long hairs.
I fight the cushions
on the chairs.
Just watch me race
right up the s...   ... shower?

Once I chewed
a stick of chalk.
I get bored
when the family talk.
Then someone takes me
for a w...   ... wheelbarrow?

Wes Magee

The View from my Window

Ali's built a den up in her attic,
Gary Farthing's got a gang hut in his father's shed,
Becky's built a bungalow in a nearby beech tree,
and Hassan has a hideaway where grown-ups dare not tread.

Inge's built an igloo out of used egg boxes,
Dougal's dug a dug-out beneath his parents' bed,
Tessa's made a tent out of blankets and a clothes-horse,
and Cecil has a cell in his cellar – so he's said.

Henry's headquarters are in his granddad's old wardrobe,

Jackie has a shack made from crates she's painted red,
Camara's made a lair in the cupboard under the stairs,
and me...

I've this fully furnished universe...

here in my head...

... instead.

David Horner

Under the Bed

"Clear up your room
   Or else ..." Mother said
"And start with the rubbish
   That's under your bed."

Abacus with wooden beads
Badges, one still pinned to a hat
Crisp packet, empty, salt and vinegar
Drawings, two of my cat

Everton scarf, blue and white
Five socks, none of them matching
Guitar string, I think it's a G
Halloween mask, with sores that look catching

Invitation to a fancy dress party
Joke books, covers bent
Kite, red Chinese dragon
Letters, half written, never sent

Marbles, three orange, two green
Notebook with the score of some game
Oxo tin, red, full of stamps
Photo from school, still in its frame

Quill pen made from a blackbird's feather
Radio, no adapter, batteries flat
Sandals, sun bleached, still sandy
Tinsel from Christmas, wound in a plait

Umbrella, yellow and red
Verses of poems I'll finish someday
Wrappers from toffees long eaten
Xylophone that no one could play
Yesterday's spelling test, five wrong
Zodiac jigsaw, one piece gone astray

Mum threatened to get
    a black bag from the shed
And throw out all the treasures
    from under my bed.

Angela Holden

It's Time for Bed

It's time for bed, it's time for bed!
But just a minute mum
There's the hamster to be fed!

It's time for bed, it's late you know!
But just a minute mum
I've only one more page to go!

It's time for bed, it's time for bed!
But just a minute mum
I could have a drink – you said!

It's time for bed, we made a rule …
But just a minute mum
I've got to get my things for school!

It's time for bed, it's time for bed!
But just a minute mum
I've got to get my things for school,
I could have a drink – you said,
I've only one more page to go,
And there's the hamster to be fed!
Ouch! Okay!
I was going anyway!

Trevor Millum

The Tale of the Leprechauny Man and the Unsuccessful Fishery Expedishery

The
par-
tickle-u-lar-
ly
leprechauny man
tookle his tickle tackle
and went forth to outwit fishes
(the water people).
Sat sandwich-munchily
On his tripodal stool
dangly into the fishing sterream
his sterring
sterrung from a hazel stick.

Unwary he was
that no hookit was attackled thereto.
Stared daylong at the horizony view
unawarily sating his piscine
(a bit fishy)
friends
on good delishibaitle foodstuffs,
to wit
wormy maggits,

loafbits,
and wruggly squurrms.
When evening fell
(tripping carelessily over a mounting pique)
he meandered homywards
happy and fishless.
He knew that there must be a catch somewhere
but knew not where
nor why it was not to be his.
And after nodded dreamy wise
at his singing
cricket
hearthplace.

Gerard Benson

When Mum Won the Pools

When Mum found she'd eight one-all draws on the Pools,
The family was wildly excited:
She threw a big party on Saturday night
With all the relations invited.
At first, it was hard to believe it was true,
But we checked all the numbers once more:
Then Mum started crying and Dad started laughing
And my brother was sick on the floor.

We started discussing the money we'd win
And we started to think how to spend it;
And Mum cried and cried and said what a good job
That we hadn't forgotten to send it.
Grandma and Granddad could have a new house
With a garden and views of the sea;
And Great-Uncle Ernie could have a new car
With a phone and a colour TV.

Then Mum went on crying to think of the money:
She'd never do housework again;
And my brother kept saying his tummy felt funny,
But he wanted a ride on a train.
Myself, I decided to travel the world,
Or go to the moon in a rocket;
Then suddenly Dad started crying as well,
'Cos the coupon was still in his pocket.

Tony Charles

The Alphabattle

The Alphabet Serpent gave a hiss
as bright Sir Write said, "Here, take this!"
And with his keenly sharpened wits
he chopped the Alphabet into bits:
A got axed and B got bent.
C got coshed and D a dent.
E got erased while F took flight.
G got gored and H lost height.
I got ink-stained, J was jerked.
K was kicked and L just lurked.
M got mangled. N got nailed.
O turned over. P just paled.
Q went queasy. R got rapped.
S got straightened. T got tapped.
U went under. V went vapid.
W walled,
and X made an exit (rapid!)
Y just yelped and left the fray.
Z zipped off to run away.
No more letters. No more text.
The teachers cried, "Whatever next?"
They shook their heads and looked aghast,
but bright Sir Write said, "Peace at last!"

Tony Mitton

Forbidden Fruit

I

l
i
k
e

      to   to
     pick   munch
   apples   apples
  polish   bake
 apples   apples
bite   make
through   them
the   into
skin   jam

hard   I
to   bet
believe   old
that   Adam
for   tricked
Eve   her
it   just
was   like
a   a
sin   man!

Moira Andrew

If I Could Buy Whatever I Wanted I Would Choose ...

Clothes that put themselves on
every morning –
Imagine the socks wriggling!
Giggling smiles to wear when I'm sad,
a Dad who's always glad,
a cassette with all the answers
and a teacher with an 'off' switch
or a 'fast forward' button,
a dog that doesn't need walking
and opens his own tin cans,

plates and pans, knives and forks
that don't need drying
and put themselves away,
shoe-laces that never need tying
and buttons that easily work,
ice creams that don't slip off the stick
when the sun shines hot as chillies,
a new neck that stays clean,
beds you can bounce on
without breaking the springs,
spectacles to see in the dark
the shapes that frighten me,
a pencil that writes on the line
and can d and b the right way round,
a nose that never needs blowing
yet knows how to smell
and the world's only
internal, human
spell-check.

Pie Corbett

 A Final Thought

Animal Liberation

I know the world's a happy place
With gardens brimming roses.
But still I think it rather sad
That cows can't pick their noses.

John Kitching